The Game

by Bobby Lynn Maslen
pictures by John R. Maslen

Scholastic Inc.

New York • Toronto • London • Auckland • Sydney • Mexico City • New Delhi • Hong Kong

Available Bob Books®:

<u>Level A</u>:   Set 1 - First!   Set 2 - Fun!

<u>Level B</u>:   Set 1 - Kids!   Set 2 - Pals!

<u>Level C</u>:   Set 1 - Wow!

Ask for Bob Books at your local bookstore, visit www.bobbooks.com, or call: 1-800-733-5572.

ISBN 0-439-17584-4

12 11 10 9 8   3 4 5/0
Printed in China.   10

Jane had a ball and a bat.
Jane liked to play baseball. She
liked to pitch the ball. She liked
to hit the ball. She liked to run.

She called James
and Jake and Dave
and Kate. "Let's play
ball," she said.
The game began.

Jane hit the ball. Dave ran and ran. He got the ball. Jane ran to the base. She ran as fast as she could.

Kate was playing first base.
Dave threw the ball to Kate.

Jane made it to the base.
Jane was safe on first base.

Jake threw the
ball over the plate.
James hit the ball hard.

Kate ran and ran.
Kate got the ball.
She threw it to the base.

James slid. James made it. He is O.K.

Jake made a long hit.
He ran and ran.
He got a home run.

The ballgame went on
and on. The game went
on until the sun set.

Then Dave gave the ball and
bat to Jane. The players were
tired. The players were happy.

Jane took the ball and bat.
Jane went home. That was
the end of the game.

The End

Book 1 contains:

Silent E:

a - e	Jane
o - e	home
i - e	like